PowerPoint Eulogy

Mark Wilson

First published April 2021 by Fly on the Wall Press
Published in the UK by Fly on the Wall Press
56 High Lea Rd
New Mills
Derbyshire
SK22 3DP

www.flyonthewallpress.co.uk
Copyright Mark Wilson © 2021
ISBN: 9781913211455

To the friends and family that keep me going

A pear-shaped man in a khaki, burlap business suit stands in front of an uninterested audience, eulogizing a deceased coworker. His nipples bleed through the fabric, but the audience remains unconcerned, they sit obediently and limply in ergonomically correct chairs, around a dusty projector. Several other faceless presenters will eventually recount their own uninspired experiences with the former employee.

Three hours have been allotted to mourn the death of someone they had all grown to tolerate over the years. Three hours of corporate jargon and indiscernible platitudes to celebrate the life of a seventy-year-old man who no one really knew. Bar graphs and pie charts are laid onto his poorly-made plywood coffin, with the hope that he'll be able to do one last round of pointless analysis in the afterlife.

His pathetic life has been distilled into a hastily-made PowerPoint presentation, complete with outdated animations. As the presentation bludgeons on, colleagues start to realize that certain slides in the presentation are about themselves. They begin to wonder if they are all dead. They realize that their lives under the fluorescent lights are as sad as the elderly man lying in the coffin. As the slides and animations increase in speed, their strobe euthanizes any desire to feel and the employees return to their desks.

Three hours until the next meeting. Three hours until the next eulogy.

Slide 1 (welcome)

We had a recurring strategy meeting that he never showed up for
And I never knew what we were meant to be strategizing
The meeting simply existed for as long as I could remember
And still exists since his passing
Though now there isn't the same dread
That he would show up
Maybe he sent me the meeting as a gift
Knowing that he could provide relief
When he failed to appear
Knowing that the happiness experienced by his absence was really
All I had left
When I didn't see his sagging face
Or constipated walk
I could sit in the dark conference room
And consider leaving
Though I never would
Now the meeting is a portal for me into true nothingness
A block of time that I reverently perform the ritual of waiting for
Someone who would never come

Slide 2

It was Christmas time, so he decided to dress up like Santa
Though the costume was more just a pair of soiled
Red sweatpants
Giving each of us a one hundred dollar bill
From his stained wallet
We thought he'd been given the money from corporate
But it ended up being his life savings
To think that he had worked so long and saved so little
I spent the hundred on cigarettes and pornography
He starved for the rest of the month
Losing a significant amount of weight
We all told him he looked good
Even though his body was eating itself

Slide 3

He vomited white bile onto a breakfast pastry
And sat back into his chair
Folding his hands into a triangle
"Game changing," he said and motioned towards the screen
Containing several indistinguishable graphics
He planted his face into the table and consumed the now
Moist scone with several sickening inhales
Furiously licking his lips, he fastened his worn suitcase
And stood
He flicked his business card across the table
And left
"Bill Motluck" was written on the card
With no other adornment
We hired him on the spot, even though he didn't want the job
He still eats his pastries like this
But no one is quite sure what his purpose is
In relation to the department

Slide 4

He wasn't religious
But some days he said we would die for working here
Die for crucifying a country
Rot in hell for suffocating dreams and freedom
We created stock photos of landscapes
And people drinking coffee
But he condemned us all the same
I'm not saying we didn't deserve it
But an eternity of suffering
Is a lot to pay for what we did

Slide 5

He ate at *Subway* once a week
And savored every bite of the five-dollar sandwich
He said sometimes you have to live a little
His living wasn't much
His living wasn't world travel
Or elaborate celebration
Or a wife and kids
Or creating anything of consequence
His living was eating a barely-warmed sandwich
Letting his fingers sink into the damp bread
And dreaming about the next time
He would dutifully recite his order
And hold the thing he loved most once more

Slide 6

Every few months another vertebrae collapsed
Depositing bone matter into the soiled fabric
Of an outdated chair
The permanent migration to the floor
Was unpleasant at first
But after some time, I realized I would rather lay than sit
So I cherished the destruction
And fantasized about the day in which
My head would disappear amongst my shapeless skin folds and
Become lubricant for the plastic wheels that would propel the
Next resident into a similar
State of indifference

Slide 7

I'm peeing blood at the office urinal again
I think my kidneys are failing
But I have a Kung Pao chicken *Lean Cuisine* for lunch
And a significant presentation this afternoon
So the stained urinal and rotting organs barely matter

Slide 8

He kept a garden of
Dying dandelions next to his desk
Thousands of tiny white globes
And exposed umbrellas of seeds
Swayed in the stale air-conditioned air
Waiting for their chance
To impregnate the stained carpeting
Or skid-marked fibers of someone's threadbare sweater

With the right gust
They would fulfill their modest destiny
Creating a feathery wonderland of allergens
That reminded him of home
He liked the idea of us living in a snow globe
Where the seasons never changed
And days passed without notice
And the white noise machines
Were capable of whispering salvation
Where we were all comfortable in our
Own inconsequence
Aware that the actions inside our homemade
Souvenir gift shop ornament
Didn't really matter all that much
He said those were the best days
On those days he would hum *Silent Night*
While the rest of us took allergy medication
And waited for the next storm

Slide 9

He spoke about the weather with the
Pride of a first-time father
When it rained, he would stand at the window
And name the drops
And say he was a grandfather
He would make comments like, "must have been some
Good-looking parents"
In reference to the grey sky and the precipitation
That spat from it
When it was sunny, he would stare into the sun until
He couldn't see
And return to his desk as though responsible for its glow
As though responsible for the life it nourished
He would sometimes cry looking at the Doppler radar
As though the colorful ink blots were taking their first steps
He had wallet-sized pictures printed
And lamented over the weekly forecast
He would show them to people
And mention how he couldn't believe
How big they were getting
He would return home after a long day
And read bedtime stories to any remaining clouds

Intermission

A man in a fancy suit delivers a well-made presentation on
Q3 financial results
He closes with a pie chart that indicates his marriage is failing and
His kids resent him
He receives a standing ovation
And some audience members cry at the beauty of it all
He's fired the next day
And goes home to drink gin and masturbate to timeshares in Orlando

Slide 10

We were on a project deadline
And he was nice enough to offer
A caffeine run
He dutifully took our orders
Even asking if we wanted cream and sugars
And returned moments later
Without coffee or tea
But with a fistful of melted Adderall
Bleeding orange onto the conference table
From his perspiring, shaking hand
He was the first to take one
But we all followed suit
It was on that day we learned he had ADHD
Or just took unprescribed medicine
We never found out one way or the other
But the project got finished

What a sweet guy he was
To give us his pills
To help us complete our work

Slide 11

She would often come to work drunk
On those days, she thought the blinking cursor
On her computer
Was her dead mom trying to communicate with her through
Morse code
Taunting her for being a failure who
Didn't deserve her last name
On those days she cried at her desk instead of working
And ate plain yogurt for lunch
On those days, people talked to her even less
Than they already did

Slide 12

One day he glued thumbtacks to his keyboard
To impress management
To prove he was willing to suffer for the company
To prove that his blood depositing into the plastic keyboard
Could save them all
He was taken to the hospital later that day
And docked a paycheck for the time off
And the damaged work equipment
But was awarded employee of the month and given a
$5 gift card to *Starbucks*, for good measure

Slide 13

On his twenty-year anniversary
He was allowed to pick a gift
From a catalog
That made *SkyMall* look like *Tiffany's*
Twenty years of misery
And regret
Distilled into a desk ornament
Or a piece of embroidered luggage

After several days of painstaking deliberation
And countless emails
Polling the team
That were immediately ignored
He announced that he had chosen
A glass succulent
In an inscribed pot with his name on it

He waited for months for it to arrive
Even asked management about the delay
Who were unaware of the existence of any loyalty program
And would shut down the whole thing a year later
Finally, a box arrived at his desk
And we all gathered around
Hoping the tiny glass sculpture would live up to
Twenty years and seven months of waiting
He opened the box carefully
Noting the *fragile* label on the side
But looking at the worn box
We all knew it was too late
He tilted the box as though it contained cereal
And glass poured onto his desk

He stood and walked away
Unable to bear the sight of
His shattered legacy
He excused himself to the bathroom
Where we heard vomiting and sobbing
We scooped the mess back into the box
And, over the next few weeks, pieced it back together
For him
We put it on his desk one evening
To surprise him the next morning
He offered a feeble thank you
But said it wasn't the same
The award for enduring
The corporate war of attrition
For twenty years
Needed to be selected out of a discontinued magazine
And made by a machine in China
Otherwise
The forgettable two decades spent leading up to the gift
Were a waste
He left it on his desk anyway
To be polite
He cared about us
More than us for him

Slide 14

It was 'bring your child to work' day
And we all assumed he would come in alone
Like he always did
Instead, he entered the conference room
Proudly and with a new-born baby
He held it under his arm and sipped coffee as though it were
An old newspaper
"Sorry I'm late, someone didn't want to come to work
Today!" He said with a chuckle
His eyes motioning toward the characterless baby
He set it on the conference table
And looked around for approval
What's his name? we asked
"Bill Motluck," he said abruptly
After several painful moments of silent thinking, using his
Own namesake as the answer
Seemingly caught off guard by a predictable question
Made the interaction even more peculiar
The rest of the meeting passed without incident, sometimes
He would chew donut, roll it in his fingers
And give it to the baby
While the rest of us looked on apprehensively
Hoping it wouldn't choke
At the end of the day, he packed it into his suitcase and
Walked out of the office whistling
Several seconds later we went to the window
To have a glance at where he was going
He handed the baby to a woman along with
A twenty-dollar bill and a leftover egg salad sandwich from
The catered lunch
He looked up and made eye contact with us

Realizing he was caught
He stepped into the street and was hit by a car
We visited him in the hospital a few days later
With a broken back and shattered legs
And no one mentioned the incident to him
We all figured he had suffered enough
Through the bandages wrapping his swollen face
We heard him mumble
"Now, look who doesn't feel like coming to work!" and tried
To laugh, but coughed blood instead

Slide 15

A prioritization vote took place
During a meeting on inefficiency
An unmistakable stench permeated from Bill's khaki pants
He'd shit himself again
And voted affirmatively for a revised capacity planning process

Slide 16

On the day of the company picnic
He brought a cooler
Full of skimmed milk
And proudly talked about
How long it would stay cold for
Even in the hot sun
I tried to change the conversation
To the new bathroom urinal cakes
Or my structured settlement
But he refused
His personality was a luxury cooler
His legacy was its melting ice
His worth was what he paid for it
His purpose was drinking its contents
When the cooler was empty, so was he
When the cooler eventually ended up in a landfill
So would he
Though when his body finally broke down
The cooler would not
Its legacy would remain
His would not

Slide 17

He had a *Precious Moments* statue on his desk
For every life event
He would point to one
And say it represented his pornography addiction
He would point to another and say it was his failed marriage
His alcoholism
His First Communion
His dishonorable discharge
His fourth-place finish in a hot dog eating competition
His sleep apnea
His constipation
His Purple Heart from Long John Silver's
His impotence
The time he saved humanity from their sins
When he overdosed
When he auditioned for Hamlet at the community theatre
And didn't get the part
When he lost the will to live
When he blew his thumbs off lighting fireworks
When his organs failed
When he found love again
When he was crucified
When he fell asleep in his chair to the television's dull glow
It was an impressive collection
Even if he dictated what experiences warranted a statue
He said he found salvation in their black pupils
And oversized heads
He trusted they would get him the promotion
He thought he deserved
Months later, the collection was gone
And so was he

A single statue remained on his desk
With the inscription
"The time I went to heaven"
And I wondered if he brought the rest with him
If they carried as little weight in the afterlife
As they did in this one
I left that day and noticed thousands of statues
In the shared office dumpster
He was piss-drunk at a bar
I went in to ask how he was
He didn't mention the statues
But said he had been dead for years

Slide 18

There was an orgy of monitors unlike anything
Anyone had ever seen
Their cords and wires molested each other in a
Sickening race for orgasm
It was a beacon of productivity
Proof that his eyes could consume as much blue light
As there was to offer
And that he could work tirelessly on nothing in particular
The perplexing part was, most remained black
Seemingly unused, at least for business purposes
Their ominous abyss cast a shadow around his cube
And waged a bloody war with fluorescent lights above

When people asked about the monitors
He said they reminded him of his dad
And no one could really dispute that
So they dealt with the unsightly monitors in silence

Slide 19

He scheduled a 'lunch and learn'
That we all expected
To be a simple display of empty posturing
Concluded with a flaccid joke
And a promise of distributing unnecessary materials
That no one would glance at again
But we showed up
Because there was an expectation of food
And the prospect of free food
Can banish the mind into unbridled depravity
A sickening desperation set in amongst us
Trying to avoid our own disgraceful leftovers
Or a six dollar sandwich
Full of barely-microwaved lunch meat
That would consume us in regret
For the remainder of the month
He sat in the cramped conference room
With several wet-looking pizzas
Smiling at each of us as we entered
We smiled back at our savior
And grew aroused
At the thought of a barely-edible pizza
That he spent the entire morning microwaving

He started the presentation with playful trivia
Saying that no one could eat until one of the questions
Was answered
We laughed but his face didn't inherit our jest
His age
His middle name
The name of his third child

His social security code
No one knew the answer to any of them
And after a torturous half hour
He took the pizzas from the table and stormed out of the room
We never saw them again
I ate a tin of tuna
Smothered in flat Diet *Dr. Pepper*
And endorsed him on *LinkedIn*
For starving an office of pathetic dregs

Slide 20

The microwave spun but no scent came out
Bill walked into the kitchen and I asked him what was for
Lunch as he pulled his modest Tupperware
From the abused microwave
"Just some chicken and rice,"
He said sadly
We both looked down at the unseasoned white concrete
Sitting haplessly in the melted plastic
Its pure whiteness was peculiar
Purposefully bland
A shining beacon of quitting
Giving up
As though it were crafted as a mechanism for punishment
But even that requires intent
This was simply a man who had nothing left to give
Providing enough nourishment to complete his daily toil
I suggested putting some hot sauce on it
And he replied, "That would be nice, wouldn't it?"
As though it were something unattainable
As though he was undeserving of the simple pleasure of an
Affordable condiment
Before I could offer him some
He sulked back to his desk
I could hear the dryness of the chicken
Squeaking against his teeth from across the office
When he was done, he drank a warm glass of water
And you could hear him humming "Taps"

Slide 21

It was raining out
And him and I were the last people in office
"Need a ride home?" he asked warmly
And I nodded
Accepting the gesture
Favouring what would likely be
An hour of agonizing silence
In a humid car
Instead of a long walk to public transit in the rain
Both of us sweating
And neither admitting to discomfort
We took the elevator down to the garage
Desperately scanning our respective
Roladex of mundane conversation kindling
Hoping to find some commonality
In tapioca pudding or crossword puzzles
Or stationary
Or the pregnancy of another coworker
That neither of us really talked to

When we entered the garage
His gate slowed as he approached
A brown tandem bicycle
He took two helmets and handed me one
With a sheepish smile
I didn't want to ride it with him
Through the rain
But I did
Because he had ridden it alone for all of those years
And I couldn't think of anything to say
Whilst holding the helmet

And having witnessed the hope in his eyes
For the first time in years
He whistled while we rode
The rain penetrated our clothes and skin
Without objection
After three hours we made it to my house
He waived gleefully and sped off
Standing up and peddling into the darkness
I got pneumonia
And missed several weeks of work
I was finally healthy enough to go back in
Drinking my morning coffee
I looked out the window
And he was out there with his brown tandem bicycle
And his guest helmet
I wondered if he had been there the whole time
He waved
And I waved back
I finished my coffee and we rode to work together
Until he finally expired
I can't say I miss those rides
But I miss him in some ways

Slide 22

She opened the meeting from her second home
Discussing hardships of the
Several thousand square-foot cottage
And the absence of luxury dining items
She had a bunion that was bothersome
In the slippers she wore
And her spineless husband was late with her iced coffee
We sat and listened
Her plight was unfamiliar
But the sadness in her face looked real
A different kind of sadness
That I guess is only emotionally available to a certain few
Later, she talked about the puppy they bought that had died
She said it was too pure to live
We concluded the call celebrating several
Insignificant work anniversaries
And a picture of the deceased dog for good measure
We applauded its sacrifice

Slide 23

There were two automatic paper towel dispensers
On either side of the his and her sinks
In the wholly ordinary and painfully taupe
Shared office bathroom
That would routinely smell like neglected petting zoos
And disintegrating bouillon cubes
And would sometimes seem to be a place of refuge
For peculiar carnal urges

Once I saw him doing something incredible
In that unexceptional space
He stood in the middle of the two sinks
That inhabit the majority of the counter
Gazing deeply into the mirror
Perhaps after evacuating his malnourished insides into
One of the unwilling toilet bowls
Or gracing a urinal cake with the warmth of a dehydrated piss
Having apparently just washed his hands
And instead of using a singular dispenser like the rest of us
Who weren't saved or enlightened
He extended his arms, as though on a crucifix
Collecting paper towels simultaneously in both hands
I stood behind him waiting for the ceremony to end
Watching a man dry his hands for my sins
Watching his face go from anguish to triumph
As he fulfilled his holy destiny
A miracle for me to witness
In our unassuming shit-filled bathroom
The chosen one
A new-born king
A corporate deity

Our eyes never wavered in what seemed like an eternity
When he was satisfied with his allotment of paper
He balled them up and missed the trash can on the way out
Knowing that someone less divine would pick it up
I see him around every now and again
And he appears as ordinary as ever
But in that bathroom
He reigns from heaven above
In those moments, we are all closer to God

Slide 24

He painted two pigs with the numbers one and three on them
And turned them loose in the office
One spent twenty minutes painfully choking on a dry eraser
Before finally dying outside of the boardroom
The other remains unaccounted for
But the office smells like rot
So we assume it found a quiet corner to starve to death in
He said he did the same thing senior year in high school
And it got him invited to Nick Naquin's After-Prom party
There was no Prom now
No after-party
Just two pig corpses on outdated shag carpeting
Melting under the fluorescent lights
And an out of touch old man
Wrestling with dementia
Trying desperately to remain relevant

Slide 25

She would leave notes on top of everything
And notes on top of those notes
They sat like colorful tree bark
On the items or processes they protected
A reminder to not leave crumbs by the microwave
To wait your turn at the printer
To speak with inside voices only
To quit at everything you've ever tried
To use the designated toaster fork when prying bagels loose
To keep crying to a minimum, where possible
To not flush disposable wipes in the toilets
To accept Jesus as your Lord and Savior
To send every email as high importance
To only wear khaki on Wednesdays
To die without pursuit of the thing you loved most
No one appointed her guardian of the office
But she took the role seriously
Often neglecting other work
In favor of note making
In favor of passively aggressively enforcing imaginary rules
The one she missed
Was a carbon monoxide leak
Outside of the conference room labeled "fun zone"
We all went to sleep that day
No one was sure how long we were out
Eventually someone from maintenance woke us up
I went home and dealt with severe confusion
The rest of the night
Often forgetting who I was
Or how I had gotten here
Later, I caught up on emails I had missed

While poisoned
The rest of the department did the same
The next day there was a note
Scorning us all for leaving early

Slide 26

One day he laid out a buffet of gas station sex pills next to the
Day-old bagels we were allotted
Pills with names like
Goat Juice XXX
Electric Blue Balls XL
Eat, Pray, Cum
And Genital Scorcher MAX
No one was certain what his intent was
Or why those were the ones he was discarding
When his collection appeared so vast
But, at the end of the day, they had all been taken
Sheepishly pocketed by an office trying to save their
Respective sex lives
Through a hand-me-down gas station pleasure chest that
Weren't good enough
For a dying old man

Slide 27

He tried to hide it
But the sound of water was unmistakable
The docile look on his face
The bubbles that would sometimes float into the air
And his clearly naked body
He had moved his home office permanently
To his neglected bathtub
We observed in silence
As he presented on a new cohesive, corporate narrative
His forehead glistened with sweat and stale water
The color from his charts and graphs
Had bled into the soupy waters
Creating a rainbow of inactivity and stagnation
His skin sagged from his bones and his eyes bulged
Full of the water that nourished him; the liquid that inspired
Him; that inspired the company
He retrieved a donut that floated listlessly by
And wrung the flavored water from its corpse
The dripping glaze splashed on his lips
And down his chin
He never looked more alive
Later that month
There was a mandate from corporate that we were to all
Live and work from our baths
If we didn't have one, a *Microsoft* bath was issued
We held zoom calls and became one with the water
Creating disposable digital waste
To the sound of the tubs' eternal fill and drain

Slide 28

Her husband and kids left her
That was after she had her *Bluetooth* headset
Permanently melted onto her scalp
The surgery was an elegant manifestation of efficiency
A subtle, post-corporate beauty that
Was not taken well by her family
Her bubbling skin would quiver with every deal closed
She would seize momentarily whenever
She hung up with a client
But the office surgeons said that
Would stop after a decade or so
The blinking blue light under her chewed flesh shined like the
Northern Lights, guiding lost employees through
The dimly-lit office
She had a legendary Q3, but a disappointing Q4
And most of us just blamed the economy
Ignoring her physical and mental decline
And the clearly infected head wound
There was a USB port in the back of her skull too
Where we would charge our devices
Using her decline to fuel our hunger for celebrity gossip and
Empty consumerism
She would bring in home-cooked chicken casseroles
The chicken was always under-cooked
And sometimes there would be butterscotch candy baked into
The soupy mess
But we ate it because watching her carry a full pan home at
The end of the day was too heartbreaking
We got sick for her
Like she got sick for us

Slide 29

He used the phrase, "you'll thank me later,"
With regularity and unprecedented enthusiasm
In conversations that weren't meant for him
"Can't sleep, huh? Eat a jar of hot Vaseline immediately
Before bed, you'll thank me later!"
He nudged the person in the side
As though the peculiar suggestion
Would ever be realized
Burdening them with an unsettling look at his bedtime ritual
"Baby aspirin? For heart health, take ketamine every day,
You'll thank me later!"
The suggestions grew in peculiarity
"Failing marriage? Sleep with a coworker, you'll thank me
Later!"
"Headache? Take three huffs from a gym sock full of
Computer duster, you'll thank me later!"
"Crippling debt? Sell your liver, you'll thank me later!"
"Thinning hair? Ram bamboo shoots under your toenails,
You'll thank me later!"
For a while we thought he was testing us
Seeing if anyone was gullible enough to take his senseless
Lifestyle offerings
Seeing if he could ruin a few lives
With some well-placed water cooler banter
But when he died
We knew that the suggestions were genuine
But maybe he still wanted all of us to go with him

Slide 30

He laid a brochure on my desk for a Wisconsin Dells water park
And gave a knowing grin
A deviant eyebrow raise
And blushed quite a bit
I wasn't sure why his skin flushed
Or his smile suggested something nefarious
At the prospect of an indoor water park
Which afforded him the opportunity to eat a
Corn Dog-flavored snow cone
In a pool of someone else's piss
Or to burn his skin off
On one of the poorly-lubricated plastic slides
But I asked if he was taking a vacation there
And he nodded, licking his lips
"Late honeymoon," he said
I looked surprised as I didn't think he was married
"Didn't think I had something this romantic in me, huh?"
He explained that he had been planning it for quite some time
And was going to surprise his wife with the coupons for the
Park that evening
He was back a week later
Looking paler than ever
But tired and happy
At the end of his presentation on email best practices
He inserted a shirtless picture of him
His sagging, elastic-looking body
Standing by a person wearing a mascot costume of a frog that
Also donned nonchalant sunglasses
And a red backwards hat
That read *Ribbit River Rider*
Apparently, the name it was burdened with

He told us they got pretty close that week
And we offered vacant encouragement at the unusual picture
After the meeting I asked if his wife enjoyed their time spent
With the water park mascot as much as he did
He explained that she didn't go
And that things weren't going very well between them
I found it all sad
Because it seemed like all he really wanted in this world was
To go to a water park with the person he loved
But he looked like he had a good time alone
I thought about the mascot a lot over the coming weeks
And the kindness shown toward a stranger
Who was vacationing alone
In Wisconsin Dells

Slide 31

I saw him slide a tooth out of his gums
Like a candle from a melting ice cream cake
He observed the tooth
Momentarily taking in its long roots
And bloody base
Holding it to the fluorescent light as though
He were inspecting the clarity of a diamond
When I asked what he was doing
He didn't seem too surprised
And fielded the question
As though I was asking what he had for breakfast
"I'm pulling my teeth out," he said
"When the last one comes out, it's my time to quit,"
I didn't understand the correlation
Between employment
And extraction of rotten teeth
But his assuredness comforted me
I heard the tooth drop into an empty tin of mints
After I went back to my desk
A month later, the tin was full
And he was still there
A whistle came from his mouth
As he toiled away at another purposeless slide deck
For a meeting that would never happen

Slide 32

Before I got a job here
I worked as a stock photography model for years
My featureless, unmemorable face
Was bland enough
To spoon feed into the mouths
Of those passively consuming content
And products they didn't need
I was the heaving spoonful of plain yogurt
They needed
To indicate they too
Could experience
Contrived happiness
Or heartache
Or abject failure
And any emotion in between
My face was their face
A throbbing hunk of khaki ground beef
Capable of sleepily mowing the lawn
Or playfully trying on jeans
Or indifferently sipping coffee on a treadmill
Or huffing duster behind a Cracker Barrel
Or gleefully dropping a luxury toaster
Into a freshly-poured bath
Or finally kicking the chair from the slip knot
Tied to a ceiling rafter
Or crying whilst consuming a plate of fluorescent lights, with
A handful of grape nuts for breakfast
Or enthusiastically applying ointment
To an unhealing hemorrhoid
No one really noticed that I was in everything they looked at
Because no one looked at me

I was something that bored into their subconscious
Appearing in dreams and nightmares
And leaving them with an inability to discern who I was
I was responsible for deja vu
And double takes
Confusion at parties
And divorces
When the watermark was removed
I was fully realized
And the more people consumed
The longer I would live

Slide 33

She created a new iteration of post-agile methodologies
Something she described as 'paradigm shifting'
And a large opportunity
For us to be part of something
She described as truly special
We agreed, because that's what we did
We sent emails celebrating the success of something
We knew would fail
Congratulated her for being a visionary
And prayed our lives would remain unchanged
Because more often than not, they didn't
Later that month, we filed into a beige conference room
To determine project prioritization
A revolver sat in the middle of the table
She lifted the gun and put a single bullet in
Spinning the chamber
She put the gun in her mouth
And effortlessly pulled the trigger
The gun clicked
Signaling an empty chamber
But there was no exhale of relief
Most of us stared on indifferently
"Who wants their project to get done?"
She passed the gun to a deflated-looking man
Who I hadn't seen before
"I don't have any projects,"
"So, you're not a team player?"
He spun and pulled without hesitation
His brains splattered against the whiteboard behind him
Distributing evenly on a S.W.O.T. analysis chart
The next person wrapped their chapping lips

Around the muzzle and made it out alive
So we worked on their project
Constructing an inconsequential webpage
No one would ever visit

I got used to the death
Sometimes even looked forward to it
But I still didn't fancy creating digital waste
I didn't have the energy to leave
So I stayed
We all stayed

Slide 34

He cooked a lobster in the shared microwave once
When he said he had lobster for lunch
I assumed leftovers
But we all watched as he wrestled the live lobster
In the abused and neglected heating device
Slamming the door shut
He programmed it for twenty minutes
"That should do it," he said
Snacking on a bag of original Lays from the bottom row
Of the vending machine
We returned to our desk
Manufacturing synergy
To the sound of a dying crustacean
And later the slurp of melted butter

I vomited into my trash can that day
And it sat for weeks
Eventually, I switched mine with his
When he wasn't around
And he never seemed to notice
He was a great guy like that

Slide 35

He told me his grandpa died on the beaches of Normandy
And said our situation wasn't much different
He compared his aching lower back
To watching your best friend
Get his legs blown off
And having to carry him back to the boat
He compared his headaches from not wearing his glasses
To shrapnel shredding your kidneys
Even though I disagreed with the comparisons
He was right in the sense that we were all dying

Their deaths were for something
Ours were not
We died for a different cause
One that would be immediately forgotten
And not worth fighting for

Slide 36

After a good presentation
Sometimes the custodial staff
Would feed him sardines
And brush his tongue with an enormous broom
He would eagerly open his mouth
Accepting their offering
Until quietly going to sleep at his desk
Like he always did
He ended up contracting gout
Which he would relentlessly complain about
But he kept eating those sardines
And kept sleeping at his desk
He didn't have much else
And the acid accumulating in his joints
Served as a personality
For someone who had none

Slide 37

He wore a peculiar suit one day
And I offered an empty compliment
Hoping he would explain where he got
The nearly-transparent suit
Held together by tiny intricate threads
Revealing his yellowing skin underneath
He casually responded that he had gotten it
From a factory sale
At Men's Warehouse
Even though it was clearly woven
By a family or spiders
That had taken up residence by his desk
While he was out at lunch

I killed the spiders at his desk

The next day the suit appeared thinner
And the day after, it appeared thinner yet
Eventually, he sat at his desk completely naked
Mourning the death of his friends
That had woven him the garment
He loved

Slide 38

Once, I found him staring out of the only window in the office
Which anyone rarely did
He had sweated through his shirt
And the last remaining strands of hair
On his liver-spotted scalp
Hung on for dear life
I felt sad in that moment
So I asked him what he was looking at
He pointed to a specific parking spot
With a 1998 Jeep Liberty
"Sometimes I just look at her"
Referencing the twenty-year-old car
That I assumed to have been abandoned
"6 disc CD changer and cloth interior," he said wistfully
"Don't let anyone tell you leather is better."
He put his hands in his pockets and walked away quietly
Me sadder than I had been before starting my conversation
The rust on the Jeep appeared like the Virgin Mary
If you looked at it right

Slide 39

Sometimes, he would enter meetings with a heaving bowl
Of plain oatmeal
He would stir
And let the sound of moist oats fill the room
And the smell of giving up mixed with morning breath
Before sticking his tongue out and delicately licking
From the spoon
Instead of inserting it into his agape mouth
On that day, he gazed deeply into the bland sustenance
And interrupted the consultant
Who was evaluating redundancies in the department
"Does anyone else see my face, in the oats?"
He tilted the bowl toward us optimistically
And we looked at the lumpy bowl closely
Examining the crescents and valleys, the mealy texture
The similarities to wet cardboard
The seemingly eternal dampness, viscous and glue-like
Accepting of its insignificance
And looked at his hopeful face
It inherited some of the same qualities
And back at the tepid bowl once more
The oats contained the prospect of vitality
At least more than his washed-out skin
And tired eyes; sagging jowls
They could transform in the confines of the microwave
Or with the addition of a few modest ingredients
Those same possibilities didn't exist for him
But we didn't have the heart to break it to him
That the oatmeal looked different than him

So we laughed and nodded
And he looked satisfied with our lie
Smiling as he licked some more oats

Slide 40

We were on a zoom conference call and his child entered the
Room, excited to show him the completion
Of a newly-bought LEGO set
Embarrassed by this simple display of affection
And longing for fatherly approval
He apologized profusely to us
We remained uninterested by
The seemingly-dysfunctional relationship
He continued his apology, his blubbering reaching a frenzy
And all anyone really wanted
Was to end the excruciating meeting
He demanded his son come in the room
And look us in the eyes
Offer us an apology like the man
He would never be
Tell us he was a disappointment to the company and his dad
We acknowledged the apology
As it seemed sincere enough
For an eight-year-old
After he left
He said it wouldn't happen again
And judging by the tears streaming down his face
And the irreparable damage done to his son's psyche
We believed him
The meeting concluded with several actionable items that had
To be completed EOD

Slide 41

I asked to borrow a pen once
And after some lengthy consideration
He obliged
That was the type of guy he was
All it took was ten minutes of convincing
And half of an egg salad sandwich
It was a no frills
Clickable, fine-point pen
Brandished with a fading company logo
From before the rebrand
As I walked away
I could tell he was nervous
And I told him I would bring it right back
But I got called into a meeting
And forgot I had the pen shortly after
The next few weeks
I would often catch his eyes in certain meetings
Ripe with urgency and paranoia
I would offer a limp smile
Or a barely-noticeable head nod
Before returning my detaching retinas
To the blinding projector screen
But I could tell his gaze was still on me
On a Wednesday in February
I was chewing on the pen
Thinking about buying myself a new manila folder
Clicking and unclicking
Something about the sound
Of rattling plastic
And procurement of office filing
Made me think of him

I remembered then about the pen
I returned it to him later that day
And apologized for the delay
He said it was fine
But barely managed the words out of his shaking lips
His eyes held an incomprehensible sadness
Without anything else to say
I sat back down at my desk
I could hear the pen clicking
And the sound of a grown man crying
Though I couldn't tell if it were happiness
Or sadness

Slide 42

I thought about killing him for a while
He hadn't responded to my emails in weeks
Hadn't been at any meetings either
Or had he?
I had a plastic bag leftover from lunch and
Walked over to his cube
Wondering if anyone would hear him suffocating
Wondering if he would scream at all
Wondering if I could finally do what management couldn't
Maybe the last fifteen years were an elaborate plan for him to
Finally get what he always wanted
Freedom from the company
Freedom from the coffee that burned his tongue everyday
Freedom from the beige pants that he wore for so long that
They were a part of him
Maybe he hated us as much as we hated him
The last *high importance* email he'd ever get
I lost the nerve when I entered his cube
And instead made a banal comment about
The existence of Wednesdays
He didn't turn around, so I left
A few months later, the custodial staff alerted management
That he was dead
No one really knew for how long
I'd like to think he was alive for my joke
But it wasn't funny anyway, so I guess I was fine either way
I wondered what finally did him in
I hoped he died in his sleep at his desk
His heart exploding in the ultimate act of defiance
It's what he would have wanted
It's what everyone wanted, and still wants

Slide 43 (closing)

After he died
Management rifled through
His personal effects
Like they always did
When one of us expired
In his email drafts folder
With a *high importance* designation
Was an email to the team
This is what it read

Hello,

I wanted to thank you all
Every one of you accounted
For another year of me living
I don't have a wife
Or kids
Or much of a family
Or friends
And I've been dying for some time
But I didn't think about it a lot
Because of you
This email would have been sent sooner
Without your smiles
Without your calendar appointments
Without the tandem bike ride
Or the glass succulent
And quiet toleration of my peculiarities
Because of you, my forgettable existence
Became a little more memorable

My unremarkable life was remarkable to me
So as my legacy will be forgotten
In a sea of strategy meetings
Procurements, mergers, acquisitions
And process changes
Just know
That I won't forget the tiny things you did for me
To make my short time on this earth and long time at this company
A good one
I hope one day you find the peace I have

Kindest regards,
Bill Motluck

Author Biography

Mark Wilson is a Chicago based author and visual artist, often illustrating his own writing. Some examples of his work accompany this book! His writing focuses on the eternal consumption of content and the monotony of the modern age. He is the creator of a popular absurdist culture blog onetie-alltie.com/ blog/ and his art and prose have been featured in journals including Burning Jade Press and Misery Tourism.

His second poetry book arrives in late spring and is called "Until No Crevice Remained" published by Orbis Tertius.

Enjoy the rest of our 2021 Shorts Season:

Pigskin by David Hartley

Something strange is happening to the animals on the farm.

A pig becomes bacon, chickens grow breadcrumbs, a cow turns to leather, a goat excretes cheese. As food becomes scarce and the looming 'pot-bellies' threaten to invade the safety of the sty, Pig knows he must get to the bottom of this strange phenomenon or face imminent death. Reminiscent of Animal Farm and darkly satirical, David Hartley interrogates the ethics of farming and the potential problems of genetic engineering, asking important questions about our relationship to the food — or animals — we eat.

"Pigskin is a knife-sharp, knowing fable about animal instincts and human ingenuity. David Hartley has a gift for creating stories that leave scars."

- Aliya Whiteley, author of The Loosening Skin

Muscle and Mouth by Louise Finnigan

"A beautifully written and compelling story"

- Kerry Hudson, Award-Winning Author of 'Lowborn'

"Muscle and Mouth made me feel the fracture of my own northern identity deep in my gut. It made me ache for home. It reminded me that leaving a place means giving pieces of yourself away; your rawness, your language and a certain kind of love. Louise Finnigan is

a writer to watch."

- Jessica Andews, Author of 'Saltwater' and Winner of 2020 Portico Prize

Jade is prepping an A-Level assignment, all her sights set on Durham University. She's told she has to 'prove herself' and keep her away from the unsavoury types she calls her best friends. Yet Jade is reluctant to shun her corner of Manchester, where she finds the land rich, 'dark with energy'.

Hassan's Zoo by Ruth Brandt

Hassan's Zoo

When American soldiers invade Iraq searching for weapons of mass destruction, Kesari the Bengal tiger and other wildlife are at the mercy of guns and keeper, Hassan.

Entrenched in perpetual fear, Hassan must exercise Godly powers over his creatures in his attempts to save them - and himself.

A Village in Winter

"Mrs Gregory said to leave Frizz and his mum be for a while. Stop pestering. That poor woman with that lad."

In the chill of winter, the villagers play by the river, their play as harsh as the ice.

How To Bring Him Back by Claire HM

'If I was going to cast a spell tonight, this night of a full arse moon as stark and crunchy as a ten-day crust of snow, I'd start by telling the earth to spin in the opposite direction.

By what power?

By the power of my pen.'

'How to Bring Him Back' is a journey into a darkly humorous love triangle. It's 90s Birmingham and Cait is post-university, aimless and working in a dive bar. She's caught between Stadd, who's stable, funny, compatible as a friend, and her compulsive sexual attraction with Rik. Present day Cait picks up her pen, on her yearly writing retreat to Aberystwyth, and addresses an absent Stadd with the lessons she has learnt from her past.

Exploring the dynamics of desire and consent while reflecting upon the damage people can inflict on each other in relationships, Claire is an exciting and bold writer for the modern age.

The Guts of a Mackerel by Clare Reddaway

"Who's Bobby Sands?" she asked, as she laid the fish on the face of a smiling young man with long wavy hair. "And what's a hunger strike?"

On a family holiday to her dad's Irish homeland, Eve's concerns about impressing local boy Liam are confronted by the stark reality of political and personal divisions during the Troubles. Former friends have turned into enemies, and this country of childhood memory is suddenly a lot less welcoming.

About Fly on the Wall Press

A publisher with a conscience.
Publishing high quality anthologies on pressing issues,
chapbooks and poetry products, from exceptional poets
around the globe.
Founded in 2018 by founding editor, Isabelle Kenyon.

Other publications:

Please Hear What I'm Not Saying (February 2018. Anthology,
profits to Mind.)

Persona Non Grata (October 2018. Anthology, profits to
Shelter and Crisis Aid UK.)

Bad Mommy / Stay Mommy by Elisabeth Horan
(May 2019. Chapbook.)

The Woman With An Owl Tattoo by Anne Walsh Donnelly
(May 2019. Chapbook.)

the sea refuses no river by Bethany Rivers
(June 2019. Chapbook.)

White Light White Peak by Simon Corble
(July 2019. Artist's Book.)

Second Life by Karl Tearney
(July 2019. Full collection)

The Dogs of Humanity by Colin Dardis
(August 2019. Chapbook.)

Small Press Publishing: The Dos and Don'ts by Isabelle Kenyon
(January 2020. Non-Fiction.)

Alcoholic Betty by Elisabeth Horan
(February 2020. Chapbook.)

Awakening by Sam Love

(March 2020. Chapbook.)

Grenade Genie by Tom McColl

(April 2020. Full Collection.)

House of Weeds by Amy Kean and Jack Wallington

(May 2020. Full Collection.)

No Home In This World by Kevin Crowe

(June 2020. Short Stories.)

How To Make Curry Goat by Louise McStravick

(July 2020. Full Collection.)

The Goddess of Macau by Graeme Hall

(August 2020. Short Stories.)

The Prettyboys of Gangster Town by Martin Grey

(September 2020. Chapbook.)

The Sound of the Earth Singing to Herself by Ricky Ray

(October 2020. Chapbook.)

Mancunian Ways (Anthology of poetry and photography)

Inherent by Lucia Orellana Damacela

(November 2020. Chapbook.)

Medusa Retold by Sarah Wallis

(December 2020. Chapbook.)

We Are All Somebody compiled by Samantha Richards (Profits to Street Child United)

Social Media:

@fly_press (Twitter)

@flyonthewall_poetry (Instagram)

@flyonthewallpress (Facebook)